THE CARDIFF GIANT

THE CARDIFF GIANT

Richard A. Boning

Illustrated by
Joseph Forte

The Incredible Series

Dexter & Westbrook, Ltd., Baldwin, New York

To

Albert J. Harris

Stub Newell peered through the dusk at the large coffin-like box on the wagon. He shuddered. "I've changed my mind," he quaked. "I can't let you bury that thing on my farm. What if someone finds out? Suppose folks learn that I was in on it with you? We could go to jail!"

George Hull, Stub's brother-in-law, was a persuasive man. He soothed Stub's fears with honeyed words. "They'll never know," he coaxed. "Just think of the money you'll make."

Hull, a prosperous tobacco dealer from nearby Binghamton, New York, had just arrived with the huge box on the wagon. A team of four horses had strained to bring it up to the farmhouse. "It's sort of a practical joke," he explained. "Besides, you can't go back on me now. You promised."

Stub was afraid, but when his brother-in-law pressed some money into his hand, he forgot his fears. "I hope it turns out all right. . . ." There was still doubt in his voice.

"A year from now you're going to be a rich man," Hull promised.

"But can't you tell me what's in the box?" Stub asked. "It's awful big."

"No," Hull answered firmly. "Dig it up a year from now. Then you'll find out. Better yet, get someone else to dig it up, sorta 'by accident.' I'll show up then. Understand?" He winked at Stub.

"We've got to get it off the wagon and bury it behind your barn," added Hull. "We'll unload it just as soon as it gets a little darker. It's heavy. Get some fellows to help — fellows who'll keep their mouths shut."

One year later — on October 16, 1869 — the entire valley was buzzing with excitement. Something strange — something awesome had been unearthed by well diggers on the Newell farm near the small town of Cardiff, New York.

A giant man of stone had been discovered. And what a man! He was more than ten feet long and weighed a ton and a half! Neighbors pointed out in hushed tones, "He looks so lifelike. He must have lived — a real man who turned to stone."

It was agreed that he belonged to a race of giants who had once walked the earth.

Following Hull's instructions, Stub Newell was conveniently in town on the day of the "discovery." Before leaving the farm, he had instructed Gid Emmons and Hank Nichols to dig a well behind his barn. He had marked the exact spot.

Upon returning, Stub sighted a crowd around Hank and Gid. "Hey, Stub!" shouted Hank. "Look what we dug up. You won't believe it!" Even though Stub was prepared for a shock, the sight took his breath away. It was so huge — so human! Only then did Stub Newell realize what Hull had meant when he said, "You'll find out." Now he knew.

"A fossil!" someone breathed. "A human fossil!"

Suddenly Stub lost his nerve. "Cover it up," he rasped. "It ain't natural. Leave it buried."

The well diggers disagreed. "People will want to see it. It's probably worth money."

Newell steadied himself — and agreed. Lord, the thing looked so real it seemed as if it would rise right up from the grave and start walking around the farm!

Word spread with amazing speed. People hurried to the scene of the discovery from every direction. Stub Newell wasted no time. Quickly he made a sign and nailed it to the gate — "Fifty Cents Admission." Then he hitched up his team and hastened to town to see about buying a large tent.

As Stub left, he heard Nichols explaining to the growing crowd how he and Emmons had uncovered the giant while digging a well behind the barn. "That stone giant used to be a big Injun!" Hank said. The well digger reminded his eager listeners that the Onondaga Indian Reservation was just four miles away.

Soon the giant was properly protected from the sun by an expensive white tent. Under the pale light he looked even more alive. People spoke in hushed tones. Some removed their hats as if at a funeral.

That evening Hull returned just as he had promised on that October night a year before. He and Stub went over the day's receipts. Hull's eyes danced greedily as he listened to his brother-in-law's description of the crowds. They sparkled when he saw the money that had been collected.

"Take this," said Hull, handing a paper to his brother-in-law. "Memorize it. Use it when you tell them about our marvelous stone man."

Stub was still nervous. "I don't like this blamed thing a bit." he whined.

Hull laughed. "Stop worrying. You're making money, aren't you?"

"Fat lot of good that'll do if anyone finds out. You don't know it yet, but there are some ministers comin' here tomorrow to have a look. What if they find out that . . .?" His voice trailed off.

"It'll work out all right." Hull pocketed most of the money but shoved a few bills into Newell's hand.

The next day the ministers spent hours closely examining the giant man of stone. One of them spoke solemnly. "These are the remains of a real person — one who lived long ago."

The crowd murmured in awe. Newell breathed a sigh of relief. He mopped his brow. "Don't push," he said. "We'll make room for all of you."

As the crowd continued to grow, George Hull watched Stub go through his memorized talk. Hull smiled with satisfaction. "Not bad," he said to himself, "not bad."

"Evidently he was carved from stone." This was the opinion of Secretary Woolworth of the State University in Albany. However, not everyone agreed.

"Look at them pores in the skin," argued an old farmer. "You never seen a statue like that."

The crowd edged closer. The farmer was right. There were indeed pores, tiny holes all over the giant's body. Even the learned men of science were impressed.

Someone volunteered the information that a nearby field had once been an Indian burial ground. Several large skeletons had been unearthed there. People glanced nervously at each other and in the direction of the field.

At that moment an Indian spoke. "I have heard my father speak of these stone giants. They made war on the Onondaga. To protect themselves my people dug pits and covered them with branches and leaves. They waited. If an enemy fell into the trap, they covered him and left him buried alive in his grave. That is what happened to this giant."

The crowd grew daily. Some came in buggies — some in wagons — some on foot. Stagecoaches jammed with sightseers rolled to the Newell farm. Special trains rumbled north from New York City. As many as three thousand people a day paid to see the giant. An even larger tent was erected over the massive figure. The price of admission was raised to one dollar.

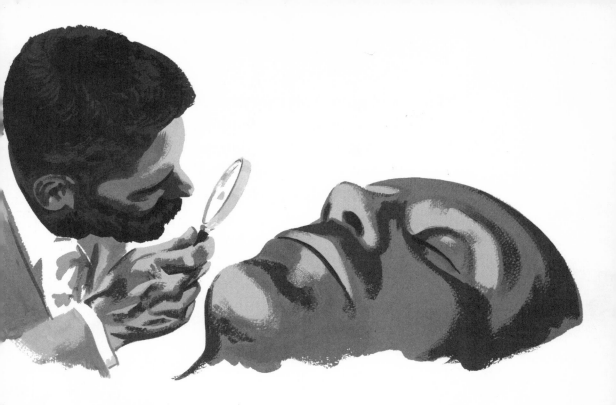

Professors and other men of learning came from miles around. They measured. From the giant's chin to the top of his head — twenty-one inches. His neck — thirty-seven inches around. His feet — twenty-one inches long.

The men of science offered opinions. Professor Boynton said, "The giant is a statue made by missionaries who came to this valley two or three hundred years ago."

Professor Hall, a state geologist, exclaimed, "It is the most remarkable object ever discovered in this country! No one can solve this mystery."

One scientist even looked up the nostrils of the giant to determine if they were those of a human being. They were!

Here and there a person was heard to say that the entire thing was a fake. Most disagreed. "Look at the stone," they argued. "Can't you see the dark markings on the legs and arms? Don't they look like veins? See how old it is. That thing has been dead a long, long time."

Additional evidence came from art experts. "No ordinary person fashioned that figure," declared one of the leading sculptors of the day. "It was not made by human hands."

Farmer Newell called attention to the lifelike detail of the stone body — the pores, the veins and even the giant's position itself. "He's clutching his body," he said uneasily, "like he died in agony."

No one could deny it. The hand of the giant was pressed against a spot below his chest as if he had been in pain at the time of his death.

That night Hull studied Newell carefully. "You're kind of sad for a fellow with so much money," he noted. For a moment Stub remained silent. Then he spoke.

"George, I don't want that thing on my land anymore."

Hull shoved a little money toward Stub. "Take it," he said. "Stop worrying. Our giant is going to leave the farm anyway. He's going to travel!"

ONE DOLLAR

Before the stone man went on tour, generous offers were made for him. Neighbors pleaded to trade their farms for the giant. The famous showman, Phineas T. Barnum, offered $60,000. He was refused. Barnum promptly hired a sculptor to make a duplicate. He billed his stone man as "The Original Cardiff Giant" and exhibited it in New York City. "Beware of imitators," Barnum warned.

BARNUM
PRESENTS
THE ORIGINAL
CARDIFF GIANT

George Hull had already sold part of his interest in the stone wonder to a group of businessmen. Together they tried to sue Barnum. The famous showman replied that he had merely made a duplicate of a fake. "You can't sue me for making a hoax of a hoax," he stated.

As each side claimed to own the original Cardiff Giant, the public took a fresh interest. So did newspaper reporters.

Soon it was discovered that George Hull had purchased a large block of gypsum from a quarry in Iowa. Freight records traced the shipment to Chicago. Other records showed that a sculptor of that city had been employed to fashion the huge stone block into a human form. When completed, the statue was bathed in sulphuric acid to make it look old. Mallets tipped with needles were used to create "pores." People signed papers declaring that they had actually seen the large figure itself on its way to the Onondaga Valley in New York State. "MYSTERY SOLVED!" screamed the headlines. "CARDIFF GIANT A HOAX!"

When the newspapers printed the entire story, the nation rocked with laughter — everyone, that is, but Stub Newell. With a groan he dropped the newspaper and rushed to his room. Quickly he flung a few belongings into a battered suitcase.

As he opened the front door, he found himself face to face with his neighbors. He felt trapped. A vision of prison bars flashed into his mind.

"You old coot! You're a first class actor," shouted a neighboring farmer.

"A — a — an actor?" stammered Stub.

"Sure," grinned the sheriff. He hooked his thumb in his suspenders. "It ain't every day that a Cardiff man can fool all them big city boys and the whole blamed country too!"

"You're the man of the hour!" someone yelled.

"And where are you going with that suitcase?" demanded another.

"Suitcase — oh — nowhere," mumbled Stub. "I was just takin' it out to the barn to — er, fix one of the straps," he replied lamely.

To Stub Newell's amazement he found himself to be a hero, and the stone man more famous than ever. Large crowds flocked to see the gypsum giant. Stub and George made even more money.

For years the giant stone man made regular appearances at carnivals and fairs. As late as 1901, he was featured at the Pan American Exposition in Buffalo, New York.

Today the Cardiff Giant is on display at the Farmers' Museum in Cooperstown, New York. He lies in an open trench, just as he did when first "discovered" on the Newell farm more than one hundred years ago. The stone giant seems so real and so human that it is difficult to believe he was not at one time a real person. Visitors still pass by and stare in awe.

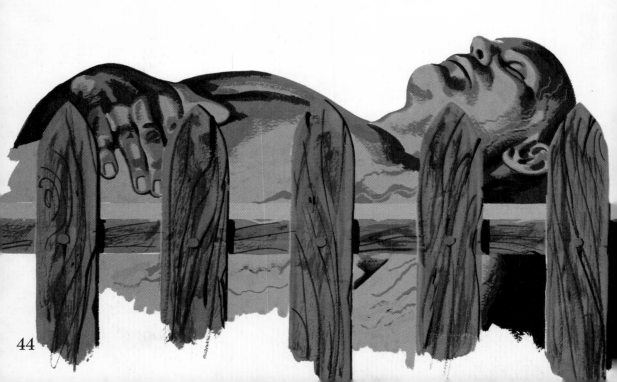

Some people in the Cardiff area still cling to the belief that the giant was once a man. "Visit the Farmers' Museum," they urge. "Sneak up on him. Tap him on his chest. It'll sound just like you're thumpin' a real live person, or at least a person who was once alive."

"You wait and see," the same people add. "One of these days they'll dig up another giant just like him. This time they won't be able to blame Stub Newell and George Hull. They'll just have to admit that there's more to this than meets the eye."

If you take their advice and visit the Farmers' Museum, you may also take a trip to the farm near Cardiff, where the giant was unearthed. If you should arrive as evening shadows lengthen, peer into the dusk as Stub Newell did that October night so long ago. As incredible as it seems, you may get the feeling — just for a moment — that stone giants lived — breathed — and roamed this earth.